WAHIDA CLARK PRESENTS

WRITTEN!
LYRICS BY
GRANDMASTER CAZ

Wahida Clark Distribution
60 Evergreen Place
Suite 904A
East Orange, New Jersey 07018
1(866)- 910- 6920
www.wclarkdistribution.com
www.wclarkpublishing.com

Library of Congress Cataloging-In-Publication Data:
Grandmaster Caz
Written! Lyrics and Rhymes by Grandmaster Caz
HardcoverISBN:9781947732643
PaperbackISBN:9781947732360
EbookISBN:9781947732414
LCCN:2019948008
1. MUSIC/ Genres & Styles/ Rap & Hip Hop- 2. Reference/Writing Skills

Creative direction & layout by Art Supplied Gfx
Book design by www.artdiggs.com

Printed in USA

Anybody can rap.... We've already laid the blueprint!!!
It takes real skill, talent and passion to be an MC!!!

Grandmaster Caz

CONTENTS

Mc.Bill

She don't want Tom and don't want Dick
she's not phased by Harry and don't need
Rick
She doesn't care if your handsome or dressed
to kill
the only man that she wants is me Mc.Bill

I'm Mc.Bill
with big shoes to fill
with me you can't stay still
because for me the women freak and some
men kill

I buy her what she wants
even time and friends
and I help her to keep up with the
styles and trends
I keep a fur on her back, a spoon up
her nose
if there's someplace she wants to be
I make sure that she goes

I'm Mc.Bill (repeat hook)

1

I've got no competition love is second
to me
I'm your number one priority
I'll make you rob, cheat, lie and steal
because nothin in the world can make
you feel like

(Mr. Bill (repeat hook)

No clothes, no fly,
No drugs, no bidin
No car and No T.V.
No fun no nothin if you ain't get me
I'm Mr. B.I.LL what's that spell Mr. Bill

I get women every day
and they're all the same.
because they all love me that's why
they run a game
On the guys might sex em and fake
loyalty
but they're only usin them to get to me

I'm Mr. Bill (repeat hook)

2

No fun, no party
No one, no body
No time, person, place or thing
can make ya feel like me cause I'm
devestating

I've wanted you from the first ~~time~~ day
I saw you
but baby I'll be damned if I pay for you
cause if sex is all I wanted I'd get a pro
and your value is much greater than ever
you know
you musn't think much of yourself if you
can be bought
cause no amount is enough you sell
yourself too short
Plus I've got more to offer than
material things
the best is that good feeling that
real love brings

Now baby don't you listen to him
he's a joke
and only tells you that stuff because
he's broke
He can't do nothin for you girl he's full

3

of it
and baby bein with him don't benefit
you
I can support your habits your wants
and needs
you need someone who writes instead
of someone who reads
your our friends will be jealous it's you
they'll envy
but not because your with him but
because you're with me
I'm Mr. Bill

gen car

yvette

It was a longtime ago, I'll never forget
I got caught in the bed with a girl
named yvette
Well I was scared like hell but I
got away
that's why I'm here talkin to ya'll
today
It was outside of my school talkin
to this fox
a croud of people gathered round

listening to my boy
Just me and Tains and the rest of
the crew
coolin out cause we had nothin better
to do
It was me, the L, the A and the All
and then I slipped away to make a
phone call
To this very day it was a move I regret
but I didnt know then so I called Yvette
I said hello pretty momma it's your
lover man
she said baby come on over as soon as
you can
I said I can't come now my man is
comin to get me
then she said I'm all alone, there's no
body with me
I thought for a second oh shit she's
alone
then I was knockin at her door before
she hung up the phone
She let me in the house and gave me
a kiss and said
give me that thing that you know I missed
So we went into her room and we got

5

but she couldn't keep her hands from
off my fly
So I made her lock the door then went
to check it
when I turned back around she was
totally naked
That was my cue to do the do I took
my clothes off and started on the pooh
Well I was tearin shit up then bout a
quarter to three
she said "Cuz somebody's comin'"
I said "yeah me"
and then the door burst open and there
was her folks
I thought damn, they could've waited till
I finished my strokes
her mother was in shock, her father
reached for the shelf
and pulled down a forty five I almost
shit on myself
And said please don't shoot ~~me~~ and
pleaded my case
said you'd've done the same thing
if you was in my place
but if you spare my life, believe me

friend
you'll never see me round your daughter
again
well don't ask me why but he let me
leave
I ran twenty six blocks then I stopped
to breathe
I gave thanks to God he wasn't more
upset
then went home and thought about
poor Yvette
~~well finally woke even more alway~~
He must've beat that girl with a stick
from a broom
cause I could here the girl screaming all
the way in my room
and even though I don't see Yvette
no more
I know she aint as fine as she was
before

g.url.cox

The Judge

You're flyin high now like a big balloon
so say goodbye now
but I'm a. see you. soon
Whether its up in the air or right
here on the ground
I got nowhere to go but up but
for you there's only downtown
Stand before me I'll seat you
if its a lesson you need then I'll
teach you
Give me a place and a time and I'll
be there with a rhyme
full deck of cards, bodyguards and
a mean sign
I'll snatch you by your neck, put your
crew in check
and teach you all what they call old
school respect
Cause you was young, chewin gum
and sleepin in sheets
while I played and got paid cause
I loved with the beats
I'm like Einstein, Wilbur and Orville
Wright

8

I'm not just down for the hole homeboy
I'm flight
I'm not a new jack clown, a clone who
aint down
I've been around and found the around
rebound
I am the Captain, the leader of men
like what their only goal is to win
I paid the cost took a toss to be the
boss
thats why my force is the cause of what
you put across
But the beats aint yours they belong
to the clowns
and the rhymes are mine so you and
the clowns
had better raise or the days that you
used to praise
are gonna put you out to pasture where
the clowns graze
I'm the Judge

Now that I got my head together, my goals
in line
I'm lettin everybody know that I'm
goin for mine

I got a plan my man and if you cant understand
you can read em and weed cause I got the best hand
All the right tools I possess what is needed
an appetite for glory and the means to feed it
A **score** to settle with the ducks who cheated
wrote a book on how to rap, I suggest you read it
Takin out you bums if you aint on par
I'll expose you for what you really are
I'll hunt you down no matter what city, state or county
turn you in just like an outlaw and collect the bounty
Make all the phonies suffer and torture the fakes
I'll have you all eating mush while I eat steaks
I'll lock you up in a cell indefinitely
your new adress is perpetrators penitentiary
Im the Judge

You'll get no bail, no email you'll stand
eat in jail.
we'll battle freedom if you win or the
chair if you fail
To think that you'd beat me is a J.O.K.E.
so you get thirty thousand watts of
electricity
You won't get no last meal or nobody to feel
sympathy or sorrow for you cause you
knew the deal
no prayers no goodbyes and no last
rites
cause even God don't approve of a duck
who bites
No kind words at your grave nobody
around
just a cheap wooden coffin and a hole
in the ground
A message on your tombstone for all you
crave
that said he lived like a sucker and
he died like one
Every year you were here you fronted
and lied
you got caught, locked up, thrown in
the chair and fried

11

so if your phony straighten up, clean
up your act in a hurry
you've got a plot waitin sucker
cemetery
by the edge

G. M. Cox

What U Gonna Do
About It?

You got it made in the shade at the
top of the heap
took the sucka way up and sold yourself
cheap
Just born and got on without payin no
dues
so now you got tossed, beat, battered
and bruised
Because I chilled for a while till I
got bored
now that I'm back learn how to act
or you face the Lord
I'm gonna slay you like a dragon wit
my take out sword
got all you suckers pictures on my
dartboard
Cause since you've been down

12

you been ridin free
And it's about time to face reality
cause I'm a rappin roadblock so get
your route rerouted
I'm back so what you gonna do about
it

I hope you stashed some money
and a couple of tramps
cause I'm a break you so hard
you'll need food stamps
I'm gonna take what you got
until your no longer hot
then lock your ass in a dungeon till you
rot
I'm gonna come to your shows
scoop up all your hoes
except the ones that are burnt
you keep those
Your gonna pay me punk dues till the
day you die
when I say jump all I wanna hear
is how high
I'll have you maytaggin hangin my
on the line
you █ like sneakers so much here

13

punk wash mine
you think your that good homeboy
I doubt it
Im dissin so what you gonna do about it

Im the MC terrorist, the rhyme commando
the real rap assassin with skills of Rambo
Im as slick as a fox quick as a jack in the
box
I'll knock ya out of your shoes
and knock da out your sox
Cause my wrath is deadly my rap is
poison
and even though you tried to brainwash
the boys and girls
they'll see through it when the word is
spoken by the rhymin lord of rap
so do heres, a token
Hop on the train or you can take the bus
then run with the bums but never with us
Cause somebody's gotta go this town's too
crowded
Im stayin now what you gonna do about it

gincat

14

Candy Store

I ran into a man at the candy store
he said aint you the kid with the rhymes
galore
he said lets break out I wanna hear
how ya sound
if ya good I'll take you to the Hollywood
town
We got in his car he said where do you
live
we went to 181st. to my def crib
He sat on the couch and started to
listen
as I rocked and I rolled on my suce
shot system
The man stood up and to my suprise
had a pen in his hand, a gleam in his eye
He shook my hand said you aint the
wack
then he handed .me a five year contract
I read it real quick said what is it for
he said you got somethin special that
the freaks will adore
if your down pack your shit and get
in the car

I'm gonna take ya out west and make
you a star
I sat and thought about this great
proposition
time was goin had to make my decision
I said I'm sorry I'll have to decline
even though it's an offer of a lifetime
If I change my mind I'll call and warn ya
grab a 747 and come out to California
Real fast y'all Cause I'm Coz y'all
and you know I make the party last y'all

JA MC Coz

"Roosevelt"

One day while in school on my way to
class
I looked down the hall and saw a sweet
ass
this is not a fib or a fairytale
I came face to face with a fly female
I said what's up baby and what's your
name
she tried to ig me like my rap was lame
I said I'm Casanova the C is for cool
and to tell the truth baby I own this school
you might see Roosevelt on the sign
but ignore that baby it's really mine
Now to get back to the business at hand
you're a female and I'm a man
Since you look so good I'm gonna let ya
choose it
heads I walk away tails we make music
whats up baby are you for real
I'll give you five minutes to tell me the
deal
After five minutes time she looked at
me
and said I want you baby that's how

17

It should be
I winked my eye and started to
laugh
and said bitch I wouldn't give you
my autograph
Cause when you didn't know me you ran
game
ya wouldn't even tell me your first name
Now you know who I am ya feel like a fool
I oughta have you transferred out my
school
I'm gonna let ya stay if ya beg me please
ya might even have to get down on your knees
If you see me again just remember this
my name is Casanova and you can't
resist.

Grand Master
Casanova Fly

18

"Amityville Story"

Well I was in Long Island lookin for a house
where I could cool out or chill
then I got in the van of the real estate man
and we drove to Amityville
He soon stopped the van I checked out
the house
and thought the lawn could use some
rakin
but I couldn't figure out for the life
of me
why the real estate man was shakin
I wrote out a check and gave it to the
dude
and before I could shake his hand
I felt a breeze and I saw a quick
flash of light
and heard the motor of the van
I said goddamn fly what's wrong
with that guy
as I slowly closed the door
I thought I guess he's just another
knucklehead
who never seen a fly nigga before
well . . . .

In two weeks time my furniture
arrived
and the house was lookin good
there was a big empty space in the
fire place
so I went to chop some wood
I brought back the wood and I made
a fire
then I thanked God for my health
and I was just about ready to doze off
when the door opened by itself
Now I did not panick or bug out
I just hoped that it was the wind
and when I went to put the lock on the
door and it closed by itself again
Now Im not a punk, a sucker, or a
faggot
that fact you all should know
But when doors start closing by
themselves
its time for me to go
I threw together my rags & ~~then~~ start
packin my bags
~~then~~ when I heard this gruesome shout
it said beat it, scram, get lost my man
or to put it real plain GET OUT!

and that did it well cause I was mad
as hell
I dropped my bags down to the floor
and said yo my man you're like the
dude in the van
you never seen a fly nigga before
I rocked a microphone to pay for my
home
and no matter how much you shout
I paid eighty two grand for this land
and no-one tells me get out
now if you wanna stay that's okay but
you're gonna have to know this much
Don't mess with my money or my weed
and be quiet when I'm bustin a nut.

"I'm Cocky"

Give me a pen and a book
I'm like kareem with a hook
and no rapper from manhatan
Queens, bronx or brooklyn
Can kick it to ya, send a rhyme
thru ya
make ya scream hallelbua like
me and I knew ya
Thought otherwise by the look in your
eyes
because your loyalty lies with other
guys
But like a book I'll read ya, got
knowledge to lead ya
dont follow my procedure guess who
dont need ya
Cocky

All star I'm a shoo in like Ewing
but a vet no better yet cause I know
what I'm doin
Number one, top, best, greatest they'll
ever be
I'm past all that, words cant describe

me
Far better than the best, greater than
the great
I rocked your block, neighborhood,
borough, city and state
in every town they've seen us
in arenas
anybody front is going to the cleaners
I'm Caz

Roll out the carpet grab yo girl
and open the door
cause Caz is in the house what you
frowning for
Don't act like I aint all that I'm a champ
and every time yo woman see me
her panties get damp
I pour forth energy greater than
the sun
not 7th, 6th, 5th, 4th, 3rd, 2nd, or 1
no number can place me, time can't
erase me
those who wanna replace me they won't
face me
Now it's necessary, highly and very
important that you know . . .

your reign is temporary
cheated on your test misled the press
I'm gonna straighten that all out
then lay to rest
The rumors the coolest the true
Grandmaster
has died, been retired or put out
to pasture
I'm a ten plus ten and ten makes
thirty
and If I'm washed up you got
to be dirty
I'm Caz

You aint bad the only one bad is me
I could be broke cause what you pay for
I get free
the things you cherish most in the
world don't phase me
your money, your jewels, your girl
who lays me
She could never say that I'm uncooth
or say I couldn't freak her out
cause I got proof
X-Rated pictures of her naked and
don't even want em.

got her panties on my wall with her
signature on em
I'm Caz

G.M. Caz

"Get Down Grandmaster"

Brace yourself soloist, duos, trios
"oh my god" puerto ricans go "Aye Dios
Mio"
in spanish or english I got to bring
this
and I know that you probably think
this is
a joke so laugh sleep on me snore
and feel the wrath of a giant
like never before
Returned to the environment to see
where the fire went
I'm not 60 I'm not retiring
a legend in the old school, better today
I'll bust a sucker in a battle the same
ole way
that I used to cause I got the juice to
and you can put the best you got against
me and they'll lose to

25

The grandest master the pope and
the pastor
the judge and jury and if you think
I'm a rasta farian or jamaican
your mistaken
I specialize in clownin and flakin
on sucker m.c.s and wanna bes
beat me in a battle nigga please
Aint no one better than the rap
veteran
and this here is just another feather
in
My cap because my rap is synched
to the beat just like a hi hat
you can try your damndest to under
-stand this
showtime is at twelve come see the
grandest

Sometimes it's hard bein m.c. God
like fightin Sugar Ray or Matthew Saad
Trading blow for blow with m.c.s ya know
looking for the knockout or the T.K.O.
But I reign supreme over those who
dream
Cold Crush got the ice and I got the

cream
I'm goin down in the books as the
one who looks
down on unrighteous rappers
and m.c. crooks
My spot is secure, my mind is sure
what else would the people sweat me
for
Except maybe the fact I'm G.M.C.
and got a harem like the sheik of arabi
It could be because I'm tall, handsome,
and brown
or the way the crowd flips when I get
down
Or how the ladies gather round when
the party's over
or maybe because my name is Casanova
But whatever the story, whatever the
reason
the audience I will continue pleasin
for the rest of my life till the day I die
cause I'm the grandmaster Caz and you
know I
am right, polite, really good in the night
and the chances that I'm not are less
than slight

27

I d.j.'d at house partys with B.S.R.'s
transportation for my set was
two or three cars
Carried amps in the rain, speakers
in the snow
spent more than I made when I did
a show
Played in clubs in the winter without
no heat.
in dreesing rooms with rats running
under my feet
The blackout in '77 when the city went
dark
I had my whole sound system outside
in a park
I paid my dues I'm a vet so dont even
try me
been in partys rockin rhymes
watchin bullets go by me
Sparkle, Dixie, Ecstasy garage,
Auddoon
the T. Connection, the Rennys, the
list goes on.
Black Door, the P.A.L. and Bronx River
Center.
when you heard hiphop thats where you

went to see vets like me. G.M.C.
the L.O.R.D. of R.A.P.
                                    g.m.Cov

                "Creston Ave"

Creston Ave. 181st. St.
It aint the best street, it aint the worst
street either
Uptown Bronx off the Concourse, Grand
and dont stand around the corner und
main
Dont let the posse catch you restin
homeboys around the way they dont play
on Creston

29

"Casanova"

I heard a rumor you want a true love
and so you're out there lookin for a new
love
Your quest has ended, your search is
over
dont look any further cause here
comes....
Casanova

I've got a question for the ladies
what do you dream of, what is your
fantasy
what makes you scream love
what turns you on what makes ya hot
Name anything that you like a lot
and it'll all be yours behind closed doors
in limousines, restaurants or ballroom
floors
If your man can't deliver tell him it's
over
time to get busy with the Captain....
Casanova

I'll take you out girl and If your real
good
I got a thousand ways to make you feel
good
each one designed with you in mind
put out an A.P.B. but you'll never find
one beyond comparison suave like
Rex Harrison
I saw you blush I hope I'm not embarr-
assing you
I can't help myself you got me twirlin'
aint nothin better than love between
a girl and a boy.
I mean a man which is what I am
others asked for your hand
but I just don't give a damn.
We were meant to be, it's destiny
and when all others are gone you'll
still have me.
I'll be the one that turns your head
your midnight snack and breakfast in bed
I'll be your very own chocolate bar so sweet
melt in your mouth not your hand I know
you wanna eat...
Casanova

Forget Valentino he ain't on
Romeo got the whip and so did Don Juan
Do yourself a favor use the number I
gave ya
I'm your black knight if you need a savior
Six feet and some change a thorobred
at the races
built like a stud in all the right places
small at the waist and large around
the hips
I eat and waitresses leave me tips
I'm....
Casanova

g.m.car

I'M THE C.A.S.A.N.O.V.A.

Check it out I'm the C.A.S.A.N.O.V.A.
And the rest is F.L.Y.
Ya see I go by the code of the Dr. of the mix
For these reasons I'll tell you why
Because I'm six foot one and i'm loads of
Fun and I dress to a tee
You see I got more clothers than a pimp got hoes
But I dress so casually
I got body guards I got two big cars
That definitely ain't the wack
I got a Lincoln Continental and....
A sun roof Cadillac
So after school I take a dip in the pool
Which is really off the wall
I got a color tv
So I can see the knicks
Play basketball
Hear me talkin bout check books, credit cards,
more money than a sucker could ever spend
But I wouldn't give a sucker or a punk mother fucker
Not a dime till I made it again........

...From the time I was only six years old
I'll never forget what I was told
It was the best advice that I had ever had
It came from my wise and dear old dad
He said sit down son I wanna talk to you
And don't say a word until I'm through...
Now there's a time to laugh and a time to cry
A time to live and a time to die
A time to break and a time to chill
To act civilized or act real ill
But whatever you do in your lifetime
"Never let an MC steal your rhyme"
So from sixty six to this very day
I never forgot what he had to say
So when a sucker MC come to bite my line

"Put that microphone Down"
(Before you poke somebody in the eye wit it) Caz

Ahh Shit is about to hit the fan Black
you can't hang so you better just stand back
Cause if you don't you'll git it
put that microphone down before you
poke somebody in the eye wit it
Stage is set time to put work in
crookie on the mic who let the jerk in
D.J. let me know
when the beats can go cause I'm ready to flow
so
Get busy with the wheels
and let me handle this piece of steel
Like the true vet that I am or ya might
get broke off
like Nickolai Volkoff
Adjust the treble and crank the bass up
give me three feet while I rip the place up
Tear the roof off the sucker
people in the crowd sayin "Caz rock the
mother fucker"
And rock it I must, my face is on microphones
~~my face is on microphone~~ over the words "In
Caz We Trust"
So I can't be simpin got to keep pimpin
cause that's how I'm livin
Rhymes are dope that's how I crack up
if you don't stack up son you gotta pack up
Back up all the shit you pop or get clowned
put that microphone down

+ Give me that microphone and sit down (Down)

34

Competition's played like accordians
taken out and dropped in the audience
All survivors gotta scrap wit me
Grand Master CAZ, step to me
One by one or two at a time gee
ya might be good but you cant outrhyme
me
Your dopest rhyme you bit it
put that microphone down before you
poke somebody in the eye wit it
Ya need a voice that's smooth like Cakim's
droppin science just like Rakim's
And youre still not done
ya need to kick knowledge like K.R.S. 1
Bust the R and B tip like the overweighter
gotta be raw like the smooth operator
West Coast you gotta be up on Cypress Hill
Dr. Dre ~~and~~ and Ice-T
Back at home fuck what a fool say
you got to flow like L.L. Cool-J
And if you want to flip the scene
you gotta ~~check~~ the Queen (Latifah)
Study tapes of old school veterans
Cold Crush and ~~the Fan~~ and if you wanna
be better in Rap check the main three
~~who~~ ~~and the~~ G.M.C.
How you gonna claim that youre great black
you aint even gained all your weight back
Get your feet on the ground and by the way..
put that microphone down..
⭐ Gimme that microphone and sit down (saus

35

Ya need more to hang on to hack this
son you gotta be on cue
Write day and night if you practice
this just might be you....
Well I'm a black mack back to attack
a wack mujack
I'll smack a sad sack track with a
stack of factual
Data see ya later alligator
vada vada darth vader cause a
greater orator made a plate a
Soul food barbequed a crude dude
with an attitude
who got screwed cause he chewed
But I'm a writer you can't take a
bite of
so light up your lighter and watch
me recite a
Dope verse or two with a curse or
two
rehearse a cue, but first a few
Minutes of funk, preferablly seven
microphones all I need is one
M.C.'s to school, ten or eleven
then a coke and smile when the job is
done
Don't stop me now...
I'm on a roll control the hoe stroll
bowl the whole toll and fold the no so
patrol
Shoot the fruit and toot toot the hc

then scoot with the loot
and knock cute suit boots
Entertain your brain like caine
and not strain to maintain
My main shit stain
False recorders break through the
borders
order manslaughters and kidnap daughters
Who are willin to chill in the buildin
wit a villain
I'm killin and illin but still in like
Bob Dylan
Democratic erratic emphatic static
I'm good at it
and suckers get gatted with an
automatic
Styles are many, rhymes are plenty
and thats as neat as Jimmy stickin Jenny
If anybody knows a trick who's slick
and quick with a lick
or real sick with a lyrical brick
He's a vic who's bound to get trapped off
step to the Grandest and ho'll get slapped
off stage
So before you say (sample: "Hit it")
put that microphone down before you
poke somebody in the eye wit it ?
                              The End
                        Grand Master
                            Caz

"On the Bus"

Well I was on the bus just takin a ride
when I felt a hard pull on my left side
I took off my shades and turned around
there was a nigga in my pocket goin way,
way down)
I grabbed him by the collar said "What's
da deal"
he said I'm starvin Marvin and I need
a meal
I said if you wanna eat don't cheat
or rob
take your ass downtown and get you
a job
He was a pretty young kid so I gave
him a break
I took him to a restaurant and bought
him a steak
the kid was really hungry and he liked
the place
so I bought him some more and let
him dog his face
Then he finished his meal, I paid
the bill
thirty seven dollars he dogged his grill

but now he's makin a livin very
honestly
the brothers on the street sellin weed
for me
He used to jostle on the bus dressed
in rags
but now he's stylin sellin joints and bags
So if you want the cheeba that's really
on
you got to buy it from the brother
with the broken arm

183 rd.

I was coolin out on the Grand Concourse
rockin my shirt that said The Mighty Force
I turned the corner on a hundred eightythird
seen a fly girl but I didn't say a word
I just continued to walk but to no avail
the girl had followed and was on my trail
So I stopped for a minute just to tie my
shoe
and she stepped right up and said
"how do you do"?
I said foxy mama I'm doin fine
but I'm in a hurry I ain't got the time

she said damn Caz that's really a
shame
I just wanted to see if you live up to
your name
I said don't leave yet cause we can
make a date
because what I was gonna do can
damn sure wait
She said I wonder what made you
change your mind
I said I'd cancel anything if a girl
is fine
Now don't get me wrong just understand
my rap
She's also gotta have a lot on the kap
Cause I believe in romance and havin
fun
but it aint really nothin if the girl is
dumb
So let's walk a while before it gets
too late
and on the way to your house we can
conversate
Well the way she talked made me
realize
she had some brains behind her big brown
eyes.

40

"Superman"

gm oz

I was chillin out like I always do
a reporter stopped me for an interview
She said she's heard stories and she's
heard fables
that I'm vicious on the mike and the
turntables
This young reporter I did adore so
I rocked a vicious rhyme like I never
did before
she said Damn fly guy I'm in love with
you
that Casanova legend must've been true
I said by the way baby what's your name
she said I go by the code Lois Lane
and you can be my boyfriend you surely can
Just let me quit this nigga named Superman
I said he's a fairy I do suppose
Flyin through the air in panty hose
You might think he's sexy or even cute
but he looks like a sucker in that blue
and red suit
I said you need a man who's got finesse
and his whole name across his chest

he may be able to fly all through the night
but can he rock a party till the early light
he can't satisfy you with his little worm
but I can get you pregnant with my super
sperm.

A Girl named Kim

G.M.Caz

It was one of those days when nothings
right with the world
I was half broke, sober and fed up with
my girl
lookin for somethin to do and wondering
how long
it would take for the next thing to go wrong
I decided to hang go out and ease my mind
told myself you never know what you might
find
I took a hot bubble bath instead of a shower
then I got dressed it took me an hour
I decided on leather fresh red and white
my boogie boots and I was sure to score
that night
the final touch some cologne I think
aramis

looked at the mirror and said you look
marvelous
Jetted out the door and hailed a taxi
said 54 and hurry then jumped in the
backseat
We arrived he said eight fifty not counting
a tip
I said don't smoke gimmee my change
face, I bust your lip
The club was really jumpin and word
is bond
I saw women walkin round with
jeans painted on
splits in their skirts up to here
leather and lace
me and my dick both agreed, we're
gonna like this place
I sat down at the bar the guy said
what are you drinkin
I said orange juice n remy and slid
him a lincoln
took a sip grabbed my money he looked
at me strange
I said psyche I bet you thought you
was keepin my change

I made my way through the crowd
it was plain to see same everywhere
I go all eyes on me
sat down at a table and one of the
staff said aint you Caz I said yeah
but no autographs
I just sat by myself and finished
my drink
I took a glance across the room and
recieved a wink
and did the only thing a real blooded
man would do
look down to see what the eye was
attatched to
sho nuff it was a girl not just any
female
her hair and eyes sparkled like ginger
ale
I looked lower to her lips then her chin
then her neck
and I wondered bout the rest and
said let me check
I sent the waiter to her table to ask
her name
he returned and said Kim and I almost
came

44

I checked myself to make sure I looked alright
and told my click don't worry we **fuckin**
tonight
so with a nice friendly smile and a dash of charm
I stepped up to the lady and tapped her arm
but when she turned around my ~~smile~~
smile turned to gloom
she didn't look nothin like she did across the room
She had big broad shoulders and her titties were big
~~~~ butt they silicone filled and her hair was a wig
She wore more make up than Boy George
and Phyllis Diller
ugly enough to be a monster in thriller
Had hair on her chest longer than my braids
and even though I got a band I don't need aids
so I headed for the door she said please stay
I said sorry brother but I don't go that way

It's the HipHop Don and
I aint Dusted but I'm
down in sure twisted
I'm smokin like a broke
stove and my mans, y'all
missed it but I'm cut work
I'm in the booth right
now I'm 2nd on the track
so nigga let me spit this
next and I'm a killa
back . . .

JP

A B C D E F G H I J K L M N O
P Q R S T U V W X
Y Z

One for the treble and two
for the bass

do aint nothin poppin
you coppin so why you
stoppin
you shoppin you keep it
boppin we droppin aint
nothin stoppin the Dons

and Grand Mizza AKA *also known*
da truth and you can
find me in the club up
in the dj booth
unless I run up on a
ya chick and then Im
on the roof

47

and you can take
it like a man or
you can lose your
tooth
I'm the #1 George Foreman
of HipHop I get high
from my quilt
Don carried for 30 years
and I'm killin em still so
cold that people freeze
light it up and pass it
please
to Grandmaster Caz
Bitch
Rick James
of
Y Crs
now roll up

'You Need Stitches'

Press conference is in order call the
media
Grandmaster Caz raps encyclopedia
Is here to rule whatever the school
Correct and in full effect and no April
fool
See for yourself live and in person
no rehearsin far better or worse and in
whatever the month and for years to
come
I'll keep a rhyme in the mic and a
fat beat in the drum
I've been chillin, watchin and listenin
rappers illin, choppin and dissin
and
Goin for broke on another man
instead of reachin and teachin
a brother man
Let me tell you lesson number one
is I'm the teacher
You act dumb I'll seat ya at the
back of the class
So pay attention books on your
desk

49

number two pencils out cause I'm
givin a test
zeros to those who can't imagine
just do like the rest of them, copy mine

I'm a defeater, born leader some call me
Captain
I bust donuts every place I've rapped
in
Waxed my opposition and boums they hit
the hiway
they tried the fly way, I did it my way
I left a legacy for you to learn from
and if your turn come, I'll have to burn
one
or two or three or four or five or six or
seven of y'all
plus four's eleven of y'all
I got rope wanna hang? nah
don't even bother
hang wit your buddy chump not wit
ya father
I'm too hot to be cool, to cold to heat up
ever been beat up? wait till you meet up
with the curator, rap dictator, tough
rhyme creator, perpetrator hater

source of rap data, boot vibrator
raps Ralph Nader but much greater

I'm a destroyer I'm comin fac with no mercy
in death wish 5, I'm Paul Kersey
Rap vigilante I'm on a mission
my competition face ammunition, opposition
keep wishin
That I retire, fall off or break out
too good to take out
I'm on a stake out
I'm not a quitter I'm a up getter and those
who get bitter had best just reconsider
For all who chose to oppose me I splatter
old school or new it dont matter
Dapper Dans and Troop suits leather and
suede
Pit bull rope chain, B.M. shit I'm paid
from Creston posse and I'm true to
my roots
I'm still rockin, girls jockin and I'm
knockin boots
I'm still smokin em like a newport
got mc degrees now tell me who
taught who you
back up you still learnin

51

wait your turn and watch me I'm burnin
hotter than charcoal check the barometer
get a thermometer, you'll see that I'm at a
All time high I'm larger than life
my rhymes are never dull they cut you
like a rambo knife
so step unless you want stitches
I'm too funky for you sons of bitches

g.m.Cal

Legend

Trust me on a buck chuck wrong I'd never
steer ya
cheer ya on like a crowd but no bums allowed
at my jam I aint havin it
I got a shot at the top and I'm grabbin it
cause my way I wont let ya stand in, I'm too
grandeen too demandin, large and outstandin
you'll have to hand in proof cause I'm a tear
the roof off the place and this is word to
chase me and Power got the funky bass
I'm a legend that's right y'all
a legend in my time
I'm a legend and not only in my mind

58

52

I'm Caz the legend kingpin of the foursome
totally awesome
strong as the day is long
a born winner a sinner always in a
position of power and I tower
over the rest I'm the best I never falter
kneel at my alter hard like the rock of
gibralter...
I'm like tungsten steel you can't dent me
go to hell and when you get there tell em
Caz sent me
a legend I started on Creston ask
anybody who knows and they'll tell you
who the best in the business is me G.M.
I can't rest unless I'm in a B.M.
W some a you thought I was over
perish the thought you ought to know
that Casanova's fly always fresh out
the pack
rhymes so hard if you bite yours jaw'll
crack
your teeth fall out I go all out get mad
and ball out rappers I call out
four at a time head up rhyme for rhyme
cause I'm a legend in my time
I'm a legend

53

- Grandmaster

~~[crossed out]~~ Caz the legend old school veteran
I got the title Grandmaster for being better
in rappin and rhymin
than all the others cuz I'm in
A class that only three can claim
MoeDee, Mele Mel and Me but not in
that same order try reversing it
Go on stage I don't be rehearsin shit
I just do it + Harlem World was the place
Cold Crush Four, Dony Dee and Charlie Chase
use to rule B'klyn. Cold in effect there aint
been nothin like us yet
To this day I still rock the way I did
when you was a kid
but now I'm solo but I don't hold no
animosities cause I got these
Rhymes poison the men the boys and
girls all know . . .
I'm a Legend

G.M. Caz

"The Hitman"

Ease back and let your mind go blank
and let me draw a picture in it and as
soon as I'm done dance gonna thank me
I put a bug in your collar
If you say so what you must not know
nuttin about me
but that won't be for long cause by mid
song you will see that I'm on and be
warned
I'm not a sucker new jack to be tested
I mastered my craft and you thought
that I left it
You sleep deep so doze on cause with
dope clothes on
I'm here when the shows on so bring
all the hoes on
the scene of the crime sight while I
win the rhyme fight
bask in the limelight cause I'm at a
prime height and wait
I got the look you wanna know better
its too cold for shorts and too hot for
sweaters
The cap is legit, words fit and even

55

when Im lit youre sure to get a hit
Cause Im the Hitman

Im too cool to fool and too hot to burn
and full grown heads are flown when
its my turn
and like a pimp get paid when a hoe
turn a trick
I get a grip Im always sayin somethin
slick
Mow down my opposition like a sherman
tank
my mind be paintin pictures while yours
draws a blank
To be frank, theres somethin in the water ya
drank
to make ya wanna go toe to toe with you
know who
The innovator who keeps the train on
track
Grandmaster Caz wack, imagine that
I know its hard to imagine me wack
Its a pipe dream
I defuse crews what I use is a hype
team
Battle me you gotta be on dope

56

cause thats hangin yourself and
I'll provide the rope
and as you swing from side to side
your legs danglin
my rhymes will be stranglin
I smoke a rapper like a joint and if
he get loud
I light em up take a toke and blow the
smoke in the crowd
any sucker dont like what Cara say...
will wind up in a ash tray cause Im the
Hitman

Im not here to do handstands and I dont
grandstand
I aint on bandstand and I just cant stand
a plastic bastard or suckers who go out
like roaches
you know who the coach is
So back up quick yall Im hard as a back
wall
now who got a stickball cause I got a
trick yall
Rappers get a plate a fork and a spoon
a tape recorder, pen & paper
and name this tune

track smokes like a chimney and
rhymes are strapped in
bon apetite and eat with a napkin
It's biteable, bitable, pitable, unforgetable
critical, irritable, non political dopeness
hope this sinks in like an anchor
I'm spreading the wealth like a banker
On top of the pile and you can't knock caz
off
a bad mother fucker cause I rap my
ass off
dope when it comes to a poem
I'll smack a rapper so hard his dee jay
won't know him
seen niggas blow up and catch amnesia
but you'll snap back when the hitman sees
ya
The Hitman

"Star Search"

In the city of bright lights girlfriends
on a mission
she's got walk on boys for all of the guys
Cause she don't want no regular dude
that is her attitude
She dresses like a Hollywood diva
if she don't know ya then she don't need ya
the fame game is the only game she'll play
to meet her you need a resume
She gets in free VIP in a party
wanna know the hoe you gotta be somebody
she goes to every concert as if it was
church
cause honey's on a star search

She's got an autograph book as thick as
a bible
and whoever's in town she's down to wait
for the arrival
Of whoever is poppin
party at the hotel she's the first to drop
in
Bet ya she'll be there till morning
with her dress all wrinkled when the sun

is dawnin
and swears to God she's no groupie
though
another girl just like her got to be a
tramp or hoe
and she's a name dropper
sayin who she knows like she is so
proper
met Bobby at a show, spent the night with
what's his name
and got a flick with Big Daddy Kane
An autograph from Eddie dined with
Arsenio
and ain't all that in fact she's just a skinny ho
but always in a party as if she was
goin to church
cause honey's on a star search

Take a number or grab a spot on line
and join the list of those who thought
they'd have to be fine or have money
and you'll soon see
you've got to have more than that a
flint movie or a record on the charts
homegirl's a heartbreaker yeah she
breaks hearts by the dozens

and she aint that fly
but got the nerve not to want an ordinary
guy
Hardworking, sincere, caring and genuine
she might get a star but she'll go through ten
of them
before she learns her lesson in life
you can be somebody's bitch or somebody's
wife
If aint nothin wrong with strivin for the
stars
but if that's where your nose is,
stop to smell the roses
And then you can go to a real church
instead of bein on a star search

I do Work?

Caz

War for territory... choose your weapon,
I'll take a microphone you take a step and
rhymes are gonna fly like bullets, lives
will be lost
careers terminated now who's the boss?
Grandmaster lord of the rhyme the godfather
of the ~~rhyme~~ mob yeah I'm the kingpin, head honco,
I rule the throne
and diss with an Iron fist like Don
Carleone
I head the syndicate of rap artists
the biggest, baddest, best and the smartest
posses of outlaws ever to rhyme
more money than a mint now who said crime
dont pay
stupid? I got dough and even if you
feel froggy dont leap cause us
you'll ~~catch~~ a bad one get shot down in
ya tracks
I break backs and tax so new jacks
relax
I do Work?

I dont have to pull a caper to get paper
make no mistake about it think you can
hang I doubt it
Danger proceed with caution, rap
extortion I get a portion
Unfortunately you gotta pay me, kneel
and obey me
Girls who try to play me, lay me and say
me when I say who's on
with no shoes on I took a cruise on...
water my yachts docked in the harbor
six times a father Bronx to Ann Arbor
Arsenal stacked lieutenants stand ready
to rock steady and get you wet like
teddy, limos, benzes and B.M.s
women so fine they got to be A.M...C is
part of the harem leave me I daze em
I never share em I just wear em out
and keep steppin on I dont let up
you dont like it, put up or shut up
aint no doubt about it @very MC
starts to fess instead of mess with
C.A.Z. I do work!

You, just a youngster, you aint a gangster
you been amongst the best so give thanks
to God you alive and still breathin
so write a goodbye rhyme cause you're
leavin
Bus, train or the midnight plane
disappear from here steer clear
don't let me see ya again
cause if I do, you will be all in
I'll have you coffin catch me I'm fallin
off to the north where suckers are
soft and run away from Caz like
chicken broth
All pride aside inside your will is broken
ya brain fried why? you still smokin
Caz is the fresh, the wild the fly and
the bold
off the rock and now I'm on a roll
paid the piper dope rhymes are riper
when I get hyper you'll see the type a
rhymes you were hearin start reappear
-in Grandmaster Caz is back so start
cheerin... I do work?

64

Slide
Ratt Pack Baby

I Gotcha kung fu grip and the whole mill,
no skills
rhyme fees start about 40 Bills, Mo kills
and casualties than a nam vet and I dont hear no
alarm got
Im slick as fox I got a brick in the box
I keep em lickin the fox so while your pickin
the locks
I got em sick in they sex they're like a chicken
with pox and no cocks assholes
tighter than Ft Knox
I brought blocks of niggas
who mad flocks a niggas
N.Y.P.D. got mug shots a niggas
who represent the real 5 mics
the click
no hoes pressing charges cause they likes
the dick
At home or abroad we put nikes to brick
and keep it movin like Meth or Raekwon
the Chef
With links thats cuban 5 mic slang is
fluid
same motto as nike son just do it

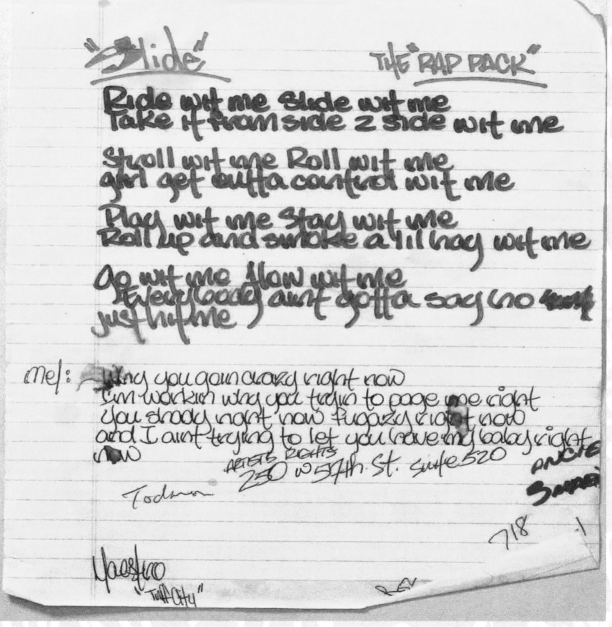

"Slide"   THE "RAP PACK"

Ride wit me Slide wit me
Take it from side 2 side wit me

Stroll wit me Roll wit me
girl get outta control wit me

Play wit me Stay wit me
Roll up and smoke a lil hay wit me

go wit me flow wit me
Everybody aint gotta say no
just hit me

Mel: Why you goin crazy right now
I'm workin why you tryin to page me right
you shady right now fugazy right now
and I aint tryin to let you have my baby right
now
                ARTISTS RIGHTS
                250 W 54th. St. Suite 520   Ancte
                                                 Suess
        Todrow

                                                 718

Maestro   Rev
"Tuff City"

66

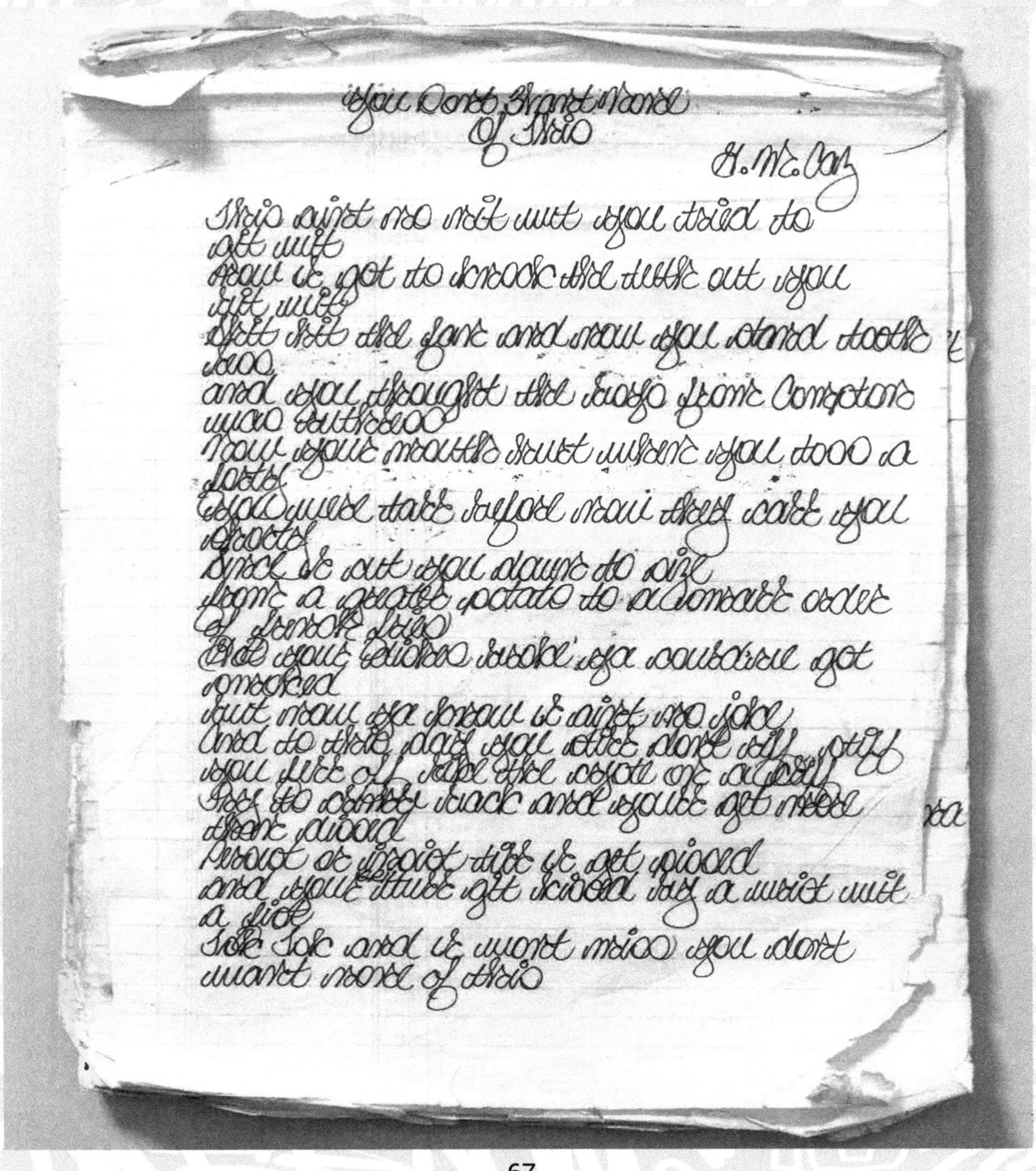

You Don't Want None
Of This

[illegible]

This ain't no shit wit you tried to
get wit
Now I got to knock the teeth out you
[illegible] wit
Shit hit the fan and now you stand tooth
less
and you thought the boys from Compton
was ruthless
Now your mouth shut when you toss a
[illegible]
You were tall before now they call you
shorty
[illegible] cut you down to size
from a [illegible] potato to a small order
of french fries
[illegible] your [illegible] [illegible] ya [illegible] got
smoked
but now ya know it ain't no joke
And to this day you still don't [illegible] [illegible]
you [illegible] off like the [illegible] on a [illegible]
Try to come back and you'll get more
than [illegible]
[illegible] it [illegible] like it got [illegible]
and your future got [illegible] by a [illegible] wit
a [illegible]
Tick tock and it won't miss you don't
want none of this

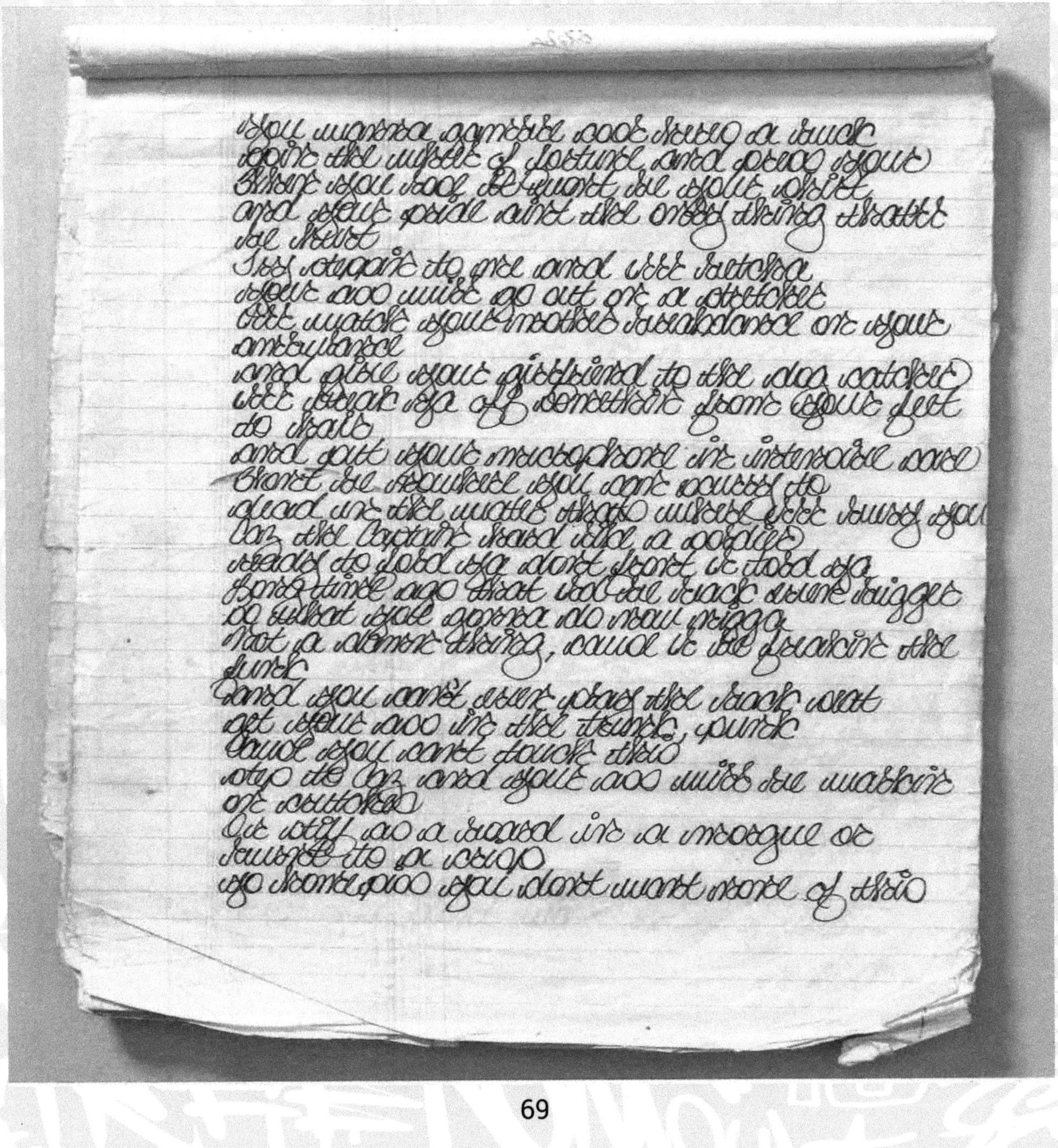

ya can't fade us baby

They say it aunt where you're from
It's where your at
Must've been a nigga who moved
who started all that
Cause I've been around the world
and ay ya ya
but I'm gon be a Bronx nigga
till I die ya ya

They say it aunt where you're from
it's where your at
Must've been a nigga who moved
who started all that
Cause I've been around the world
and ay ya ya
but I'm gon be a
till I die ya ya

I'm a Bronx nigga and I don't beg your
pardon
I was twelve or thirteen when HipHop was
just startin
I helped lay the cement and when
the concrete hardened
I watched HipHop grow out this
concrete garden

~~Born and raised in the Bx and I'm
still a resident, I'm never hesitant
and when it came to the Hip Hop
I'm the BX borough president~~

I put it in around the world son
as well as the hood
help put the BX on the map and repped
as well as I could
And I aint visitin no bitch I got keys
I'm a resident
and I aint no client I'm the Bronx borough
president ~~Soundview to Seabrook Prospect to Union~~
43rd precinct Soundview is the hood
they say our corners kinda cozy cuz
we gettin it good
You see I live back by the water where
niggas be fishin
Same area they bury you and niggas
be missin
A few blocks from the Bruckner
not far from the Deegan
And not far away from the Cross Bx.
Expressway
I'm ~~not~~ hard to find I'm not far
from the Zoo
Just go stand by the gorilla cage
and go oooh ooooh's

4 Bar Funk

I'm about to blow ya mind like Eve & Gwen
so fuck what you had told Craig a dem
It's about to pop and right here is the jump off
so the damn thing and girls shake ya rump off
P.Lee's back with a brand new bag
~~James~~, ~~Curtis~~ and a brand new jag
Poppa got a benz
four bar funk that's easy to ride on
so get your bus stop or electric slide on
Chi Town to B.X. here's the connection
me and P.Lee is hip hop perfection
We keep the track movin in the right
direction no brakes so don't block the
green lights when we're goin thru an inter
section
No parkin on the dance floor thats the
rule
get yo back up off the wall cause that aint
cool
We need asses movin from front to rear
before we get the hell up out of here

wit the 4 bar funk

3 WE JUST WANNA MOVE YO BODY

2 ALL YOU GOT 2 DO IS PARTY

4 THROW YO HANDS UP EVERYBODY

1 ~~GET UP~~ GET UP GRAB YO SELF A HOTTIE

2 THE 4 BAR FUNK

1 CHECK OUT THE SHORTY WITH THE FULL LENGTH
■ MINK ON 2 LOOKIN SO GOOD YOU DON'T WANNA BLINK
LONG 4 STANDIN AT THE BAR TRYIN TO GET HER DRINK ON
3 PINK ON BABY GOT GUCCI LINK ON
~~Grab Goin everybody back them baton~~
5 4 BARS THE FUNK IS ON LET BABY KEEP
   DRINKIN TILL HER DRUNK IS ON
   8 KEEP THE CLUB PUMPIN TILL THE CRUNK IS ON
   7 GET ON THE SAME PAGE JUNK IS ON
9 "THE FUNK IS ON"
10 DANCE FLOOR IS PACKED LIKE A SUITCASE
11 SOME WIT FAT ASSES SOME WIT A CUTE FACE
12 FUNK GOT EM SWEATIN LIKE CORDUROYS
13 BOUT TO GET ON THE PHONE AND CALL ALL DA BOYS
   GOT THE NIGGAS THAT'LL BE UP ON YOUR
   DAUGHTER BOYS
   LOUDEST NIGGAS IN THE CLUB MAKIN ALL THE
   NOISE

WE GON PARTY TILL THE BREAK OF DAWN.
EITHER THAT OR TILL THE GIRLS ARE GONE
With the uber funk.

A B C D E F G H I J K L M N O P Q R S T U V W X Y Z

Boss of da Bosses

My flows tighter than young pussy wit an
untapped cherry
niggas ask you how nice I am tell em
very
I write wit a gold pen on ~~pencil~~ pads
or loose leaf
I'm that uncle huggin ya moms I'm why your
dad got loose teeth
I tap jaws and I aint got no rap flows
I clap fours and bust ass on rap tours
Fuck you and your pets yo dogs and ~~yo~~ cats
and let me introduce you to these baseball
bats
I don't need no gats a louieville and some
space
and then watch your head fly outta here like
Mase
you aint worth the case so kick rocks and get
ya own on
We the hottest shit since fat Joe put Pun on
Bronx Marauders make waves in still waters
rhymes be so deep sometimes we dont sleep
We break nights on henney and smoke dro out of
glass bowls
and ~~~~~ invent new ways of rippin niggas
new assholes

I be nigga add the st anyone disagree
I doubt it highly. I'm bout it try me you
come away with a win it won't be by me

Rat Pack be the fam I'm be the boss of the bosses
I'm that nigga with the mike 2chains and
2crosses
I got wins stacked to the ceilings but not
many losses
and I keep a full stable but I dont mean horses
I'm a rhyme professor I should teach rap courses
I aint never been married cause I dont believe
in divorces
Never joined the Army cause I got my own armed
forces
and I never reveal sources

5 Mics

G.M. Caz

Fuck 5 Mics just give me twenty eight and
a half
cause thats how long I've been nice at
this shit you do the math
When Kool Herc was doin Cindy's sweet 16
I was a b-boy and taggin up Mr. Mean
To the days of Casanova and Disco Wiz
Mighty Force to the Force 5 to the Notorious 2
to writtin fat boys rhymes for rappers delight
to blowin up with the Crush aight
First you can give me two mics one for my
nephew and one for my Mom
and a mic for every head who said I was the
bomb
And one mic for each seed thats 8 and still
countin
and one for turnin a molehill into a mountain
Give me a mic for every rapper who ever
uttered a word
said a rhyme, got tongue twisted, bit, stuttered
or slurred
Give me 5 mics somebody gave me six and
I dissed em
you wanna do somethin dog give me a whole
sound system

5 Mics remix

At one time me and my niggas had it locked
like OZ
they compared us like they do Jay-Z, Biggie
and Nas
Before videos, palm pilots and c.d. roms
y'all fuckin Dee Dee ~~sis tong~~ we was fuckin
Dee Dee moms up
Ghetto fab ~~garage~~ in the lab comin up with that
fly shit
you did you, he did him and I stayed doin my
shit
Had more fans than summer no benz and no
hummer
my mans and 'noe from another borough we
thorough like them
hood dwellas the original goodfellas and my man
jaguan gone get the whole hood jealous
~~aaaaaa~~. ~~aaaaaa and aaa aaa~~ got a track
and three legends what more do you need
a.m. car and I'm a smoke dis like all of yo weed
step to the foursome and get ate like egg fuyung
it ain't that we too old it's just that they too
young
y'all better leave these macks alone b/4 you get
blown
like a motherfuckin saxaphone

ABCDEFGHIJKLMNOPQRSTUVWXYZ

Grandmaster rope and the Pastor dope quote me
bastard hope float me as the globe stay
splinnin the captain stay winnin and you'll
stay in landing lap will stay warmed I
blow pikes roll up in the Source with oo mics
and leave a blast from the past on their candy
ass
Rhyme wrecker straight from rhyme Mecca
~~xxxxxxxxxx~~ hiphop overlord rappers over
board
All deviation I'm still around and flow still
astoundin boes till the town when turntables
& MC is on the Marquee on the ~~xxxxxxxx~~
or ~~xx~~ the ~~xxxxx~~ ~~xxxxx~~ Motherfuckin M.I.C.
no quitter I pitch the no hitter and mics
is no trouble I triple I double I slam
niggas know who the fuck I am fuck who
y'all know what the fuck I do
I don't snitch I do shit to get rich and pitch
a bitch and I'd rather fight than snitch
way didn't you bite the bitch don't even like
the bitch and any nigga wanna battle
you can mic the bitch
get your check one two make sure your
throat is clear and make sure every rhyme
you ever wrote is clear

717
SA0295

"A GOOD MAN IS GONE"   g.m.c.

he might've been
your enemy But he was
        alright to us

It's jus
another night
for us
But dont nobody WHAT ENDED HIS LIFE
with when   A MAN WITH A GUN
a good man AND I WONDER WHAT HE WOULD SAY
bite the   IF HE COULD BE HERE TODAY
dust
He couldve He was the greatest but I guess he aint
been a light too great now
to us   he could've made it ~~mean~~ but I guess it's
             too late now
somebody's   He had a future but somebody just took
pops, maybe   it away
a mother's
only son   Another one bites the dust
            Aint nothin happy about a good man buyin the
            farm
            shot down in his prime I guess it was his
            time
            They say guns dont kill people but I beg
            to differ
            Have you mama in the church screamin Lord
            why him
            Preachers ~~and the whole congregation~~ singin hymns
            & psalms
            who got da sisters Aint J and your Moms
                          in it wit ya

Its jus
another night
for us

Shot down in his prime for no reaso

A B C D E F G H I J K L M N O P Q R S T U V W X Y Z

People use to say only the good die young
it aint just that brothers in the hood die young

He could've been the next prez ~~or type~~ won
a nobel prize
He coulda been somebody famous ~~or~~ or ~~great~~ one
of the ones
~~He~~ could've been the leader that would've
changed our course
He could've got 5 mics in the source
He might've done great things invent a cure
for Cancer
To lifes ~~biggest~~ questions he just might've
had the answer
But I guess we'll never know because a
gun was drawn and now a good man is
gone

1st.4   He could've been the next Malcom or Marcus
Garvey
but somebody had to go out just like Lee Harvey
and strike a brother down in his prime
There aint no tellin what he could've done given the
time

Niggas like to bust It's just another night
to us
But dont nobody win when a good man bite
the dust ~~he was~~ he wasn't black or white ~~to us~~
~~he was~~ ~~he mighta~~ he ~~even~~ mighta
been your enemy
but the cat was alright ~~to~~ us ~~even~~ hearf tight wit us
sometime he used to fight wit us best he'd
fight wit us he didn't even like to cuss but ~~well~~ he
~~never got real loose but~~
he wasn't too tight to bust
~~he~~
Till somebody bust back ~~and left~~ hollow ~~tip~~ bit
their ~~the~~ mark ~~that kid brown~~
and splattered ~~him~~ all over the park
He's a wrap another stat who wasn't here
that long
and now ~~another~~ good man is gone

312
3770044
MELISSA

A lot of people say the good die young
Not only do the brothers in the hood die young
but . . . . .

He's survived by his parents, wife and
daughter of five

Aint nothin happy about a good man buyin
the farm
aint nothin nice when you console a cryin
mom
Aint nothin cool when a brothers killed by
one of his own
aint nothin right a good man is gone
And you can cry I know you got a lot of tears
cause this guy you've known for a lot of years
And you wish that you could bring him back
somehow
but cant nobody help him now, all you can
do
is remember how he used to smile
and be sure the cat who did it dont make
it to trial
and do the best you can to look out for his
mother and child
~~xxxxxxxxxxxxxxxxxxxxxxxxx~~
get in his shoes and try to walk a mile

1981

grandmaster Caz

MELODY : ALONE AGAIN NATURALLY
         GILBERT O'SULLIVAN

It's 1981 and before the year is done
everybody's gonna know that we're on the
go like crazy JOE on the 7.0
And when 82 rolls around we'll still be gettin
down
with a funky dance thats puts you in a trance
you got to see it to believe it
We'll put on a show and you know
we can't be beaten
we proved that we could make ya move
our rhymes are bitten, chewed and eaten
But we keep rockin on and makin up new songs
so here we go, once again

I'm Captain of the Four
GM Caz with the rhymes galore
and I'm J, JDL with the clientle
and I wont brag about it no more
And no your not in a dream
I'm Easy A known as Supreme

87

and as its plain to see
I'm the Almighty

And we are the Cold Crushin mother fuckin
tough ass four mc's won't you please
hear what we're sayin
We want you to enjoy yourself when you hear
the four playin
So until we meet again, this song will have
to end
So let the show . . . carry on?

Grand Wizard 1981

Other MCs

Other MC's can't deal with us
Cause we are the four known as
the Cold Crush
Puttin fellas on the jock makin
fly girls blush
You know we got a funky song
So won't you come and sing and
dance along
We got the two dj's on the wheels
of steel
Charlie Chase and Tony Tone at the
top of their field
Message to the competion better
we for real

We rock a party till the break
of day
and this is how it sounds when
we play
We are the four MCs with the
most respect
And if you wanna throw joints
you better come correct
We might have to take you out
or put your crew in check
because the CCd is number-one
and you gotta walk before you run
we-ell

Coz the initials of my name is G MC
and you can search all your life
but you'll never see

A brighter power party rocker
in the galaxy
I'm the first and never last
cause I'm the Grandmaster Coz

JDL the initials of my name is JDL
and I wanna go to heaven before
I go to hell
and I'm pushin more power than
a duracell
better than the oldest and the
newest
And my name is Jerry D.Lewis

A.D. the initials of my name is EAD
the baddest thing to hit n.y.
since Old E
And I can rock upon a mic

91

before you count to three
and you know I'm makin cash money
Cause I'm Supreme Easy AD
the initials of my name is AKG
and if you're smart you won't try
to mess with me
I might have to take you out or
play you outta B
Cause I am the one and only
I'm the Almighty Kay Gee

So by now you should know what
we're all about
because the four is number one
and that's no doubt
We're guaranteed and qualified
to turn the party out

we give you what you paid your
money for
while we rock you with our things
galore
yeaaah!

To the theme
of
No Disrespect

We don't mean no disrespect, its time
we put you in check &
its not that we're conceited, its just
that we're defeated all of you
Why you wanna be around us
there you wanna front and down us
with your silly games
People come up and tell us, that y'all
act very jealous
but we're not sayin no names
now y'all just keep on frontin' bout that
shit don't mean nothing to the fans
cause we just keep on movin' and y'all just
keep on bitten' move and move
Other mc's wanna be us, cause when
people come and see us we just set them strait
while the other crews just break up
we'll stand tall and make up the ultimate
show
and we come here to let you know

The fans sometimes are oh so lost
why don't you check us out and you'll
know why

94

theres only room for one you cant get
by we take two steps back or stay inside
the come have to let you know
that theres no where that you wont go
so give me a break yay ow hey ho
and get down, get loose, get ready, get set
lets go

95

All praises to my higher power and that
automatic
...I am and am a grateful recovering addict
My ~~many~~ strength, ~~hope~~ and ~~courage~~ is
what I've come to share

and it ask that you identify and not
compare

I first started using drugs, when it was
still at dark

but little did I know it stuck my head
like a guillotine

cause if I knew then what I know
when I didn't... my head anyhow
it wanted to all down and out with a
...

and something else is what everybody used
to do

Thats when it started dying giving
games at night

a fat... and a party and all was
alright

it was socially acceptable we smoked
every day

and if your money was short you
scrapped... for a...

it got so normal the weed didn't affect
me again

so on the bright side of days keep us tired
cocaine

it didn't mean to be an addict never
knew what it was

but we the crack sniffing coke is what
everybody does

And you know the Grand Master, the head
of the crew

had its so much or more of what everybody
body do

And all-gazing and rapping got me juice
ya all

so the drugs injected heroine and the drugs
were the last (last)

it didn't know that my space was cooked
it had been sniffing for years and still
wasn't hooked

we been on tours, in magazines, made a
movie and put shows on wax

So where's the loot?
do you have to ask
Around 1985 the shit hit the fan
the group split up the second company

picked us and it said Damn
ate the weed and it got nothing back
up jumped the devil with their new drug
that called crack
it was cocaine but cooked up in a rock
that you smoke
it took a toke, and that was all she
wrote
No need for war stories there's too many
to tell
but smoking crack made my life a living
hell
made me a liar a thief, a ~~crime~~ a sucker
as well
and put me in the streets and crack houses
and even a cell
stole from my mother and my family and
girlfriends too
and everybody who kept on me it got
them too
thought it was better than a crackhead
one different from them but it showed
the same addeace and sometimes the
same scene

Nowadays one giving thanks to my
food and water
Me restoring my sanity and renewing
that behavior
And filling me up with his spirit
and forgiving the unkind remarks that
was meant to break it
My will had become unmanageable
my actions damageable, maybe it was
acid
Quick to blame that next meant all that
while binding
thinking and deciding when it my
winding thinking
That took me to the pit of insanity
drugs, it got me even though it needed
not me
it still felt rock bottom, saddamshussein
couldn't scare that me
it was it hurt myself, endangering
my health, and welfare destroying my
temple
but a day at a time one getting better
day knowing it wisdom
it hard to admit it was an addict

give up and surrender and way to
myself, we were dead it
we got to find a better way
we it gave myself a break and through
the good and N.A.
it ____ a day at a time with a
____ that ____
____ myself and we ____ not we ____
the ____ we the ____ let me ____
my girl
____ if ____ ____ know ____ ie
____ ____
H.P. ____ Power and to end my ____
N.A. they keep me clean one day at a
time And by the grace of God done ____ will
not ____, but we know ____ my heart we got
to keep coming.   ____ ____

Grateful Recovering Addict
10/31/93

"BRYCE" R.I.P.

This one's for you Bryce and I won't say wherever you are
cause I know you up in heaven and ~~where~~
your ~~now~~ chillin with tha
Tell her we miss her just like we're gonna miss you
and tell Walter, Jimmy and Irene we miss them too
We're all sad you're gone but out of you we sing
I guess if I was god I'd've done the same thing
Cause anybody that knew you down here on the ground
knew this world was ~~much a~~ better place when you was around
You were my nephew I was your uncle though
you were two years older
But brothers nonetheless I remember ridin on your shoulders
I looked up to you always from the time I was two
We fantasized about being heroes but my hero was you
You was a jolly dude though sometime you would brood
always flashed that crooked grin when we gave you our food
There was nothing you couldn't do always get straight A's
a role model for us growin up back in the days
You protected us no matter what anybody said
I remember you throwin a brick at somebody's head
For pickin on your little sister nobody messed with your fam
and I thank you for help*ing* to *make* me the man

that I am
When I needed answers or some sound
advice
no matter what I could always count on
you Bryce
And at my lowest point, when and life hit
rock bottom
you stuck your hand out like ~~nobody would~~ nobody would
~~mmmm~~ and said I got him (end of verse)
there's no way I can repay you for all of your
deeds
except pass on your wisdom and be here
for your seeds
Stay close with the family because we're all
we got
and I'll see you when I get there One Love
Big Pop
Love
Cal 2000
P.S. when I think of you all I have is nothing but
love
and memories of all the things we dreamed
of
Times when you was Batman and I was Robin

Bryce
Cabe

Ms Ingrao
DA
Mighty Thor
Milk Mob
Mal

Mr.
D'ANGELO

Fleetwood
Mac
Bob Seger
Sts Phillip & James
Meatloaf
Batman
Robin Water Guns

Rhea Williams

Stewart's
Root Beer
Tommy Bauccio

Conrad
Immaculate Heart
of

Cabbage
"Nobody mess with Major"
St Pascal's
Mercy's Seminary
Dar k Dutch

Check it out...

I'm the C.A.S.A.N.O.V.A and the rest is F.L.Y.
You see the cat who bit this rhyme ~~scribble~~
~~scribble~~ was my manager.
pure treason I'll tell you why
cause he's six foot, ~~scribble~~ two tons ~~scribble~~
and cant dress ~~scribble~~ to a tee
He aint got no clothes much less no hoes
and aint even a M.C.
No bodyguards and those two cars the lincoln
and the cadillac
he ~~scribble~~ sung about in ~~scribble~~ his song well ~~scribble~~ all that's
~~scribble~~ gone
And my money paid for that
When I was ~~scribble~~ school he did some shit
uncool
~~scribble scribble scribble~~
~~scribble scribble scribble~~
~~scribble~~
that was really off the wall ~~scribble~~
He made deal with the Sugarhill to rap
and weeks later gave me a call
He said I need some rhymes to rock off
goodtimes
I said who you aint no M.C.
He said these people in Jersey got two
for the gang
needed artifical ~~scribble~~ they picked me
~~scribble~~ I gave em to him the
~~scribble~~ Checkbooks, credit
cards and money than a sucker could ever

spend

~~But~~ he never gave a nigga not a god damned
dime
and was supposed to be my friend
it aint over son....

Back to Hook (Chorus)

I didnt know what to do~~oo~~ I didnt know
I could sue
Cause nobody ever told me so
And I pretty much put the thing out of
my mind
until I heard it on the radio had every station
Playin hiphop the hibbie to the hibbie
people walkin up to me in the street
Sayin we heard your rhymes on the radio
they robbed you and that Good Times beat
It wouldve been alright had I a copyright
or a lawyer who knew and ~~didnt~~ stee
So I deaded Big Banks forgot Rappers Delight
and did what I had to do for me

Since then Ive done a few things ya heard
like make the name Cold Crush a household
word
I starred in wildstyle plus rhyme and
reason
did a sprite commercial wit kobe during
b.ball season
Ive Traveled abroad as well as the states
rocked wit Doug E. Kane. L.L. and all of

the greats
wood battles at seminars awards wit
my name
                the
inducted into D.M.C.'s hall of fame

It was a while ago but I couldnt let it go
until I had my say
And as for me I'm company V.P. Jazz Child
simple on the way
Still lethal with a pen and a pad aint
nothin changed as Gods my witness
Except for the fact its not personal no
more its strictly business

105

"Hate the Game"

It's Mizza the hated that's O.K. though
I mold ~~average~~ rappers into M.C.s
like play dough
You right I'm wrong whatever you spel
~~say through~~ ~~Bro doe~~
You broke my heart, I know it was
you freedo
Niggas got piles but can't sell em
which means they aint gettin a dime
when they tell em
Meanwhile I be writin and think
in cip wacks ~~2 get paper more than~~
~~to be better than a nigga was~~
I did back in the days
My shit is current like electric
ity
I tour big like the U.S Victory
You come close but still can't git
wit me ~~do and did~~ wit
You got lit wit me ~~but aint shit~~ shit ~~to~~
me
I saw ~~em~~ taught niggas I sold and bought
niggas
I taught niggas I hold down
the fort niggas. support niggas

106

you should know and that
familiarity breeds contempt
and aint no nigga exempt
I was once told by my mother R.I.P.
"who was from down south she said
"never let a puppy lick your mouth"
I didn't know back then why what
she said was true
but now I do ~~~~~~~~~~~~~~~~
So fuck all y'all who can't stand to
see me shine
and fuck all y'all jealous niggas I got
bitches in line
and fuck you undercover haters y'all is
the worse kind
I give less than a fuck about you
why you all up in mine I'm still doin my
thing I aint nobody I'm broke, overweight
I'm a has been youre 3 steps from has been
while you shovel "snow bitch I'll be
skiing in Aspen
While you cheese and snicker I smoke
Ide and drink liquor
and look real good when I dress
you know the rest

107

11th. best of the 50 Greatest or

so says Blaze

One of the top 3 if you voted back

in the day

Legend status in this hip hop game

and still growin

Still showin 39 and still flowin...

I'm about to turn into somethin

that y'all aint seen

A G who dont give a fuck about

nothin but cream cream

And when I flip you cant say I

didn't want to try to fit cha

you be outta the picture

I aint fuckin wit cha

So stay out the sun or get some

dark ass shades

cause I'm about to blind niggas

got have no time niggas

Do unto niggas as they do unto

me

but I'll still be the nigga that you

want to be.

Mic slayer, ~~the naked emperor under~~
~~exposed from~~ the major
khame eager, DJ er, mind swager
dime lager, on time packer, slayer
but not a whack lp that alert and flame
they call me ~~Donte~~ baby cause I got
game
~~JESUS~~
More papers than Austin, more rings
than Boston
Dopes they get forced in whores they
get tossed and turned out like...
Olivia, coke from Bolivia,
and niggas wit no mind of they own
they get blown like
Johns and ~~erobs~~ we set off like
nitro
bum rush the stage pop crist and
I ain't deo
collect the money split it up with
~~tulia~~, whip, mel and blane
and be gone black man be gone !
smoke like a stove and be out till the
next time
~~somm~~ ~~da~~ need know the flava
or who got the best rhyme

Mr. ~~a~~ !

A LOT OF RAPPERS ARE WACK....

THAT'S WHY I STICK EM AND STUCK EM

TRICK EM AND FUCK EM AND VICK EM DICK EM

AND DUCK EM AND SICK EM KICK EM AND BUCK BUCK EM

I'M NOT WIT THAT ILLIGIT BULLSHIT SHOT FROM THE HIP OR SPIT
FROM THE PULPIT

A BORN LEADER TENS ON THE RHYME METER

I PACK A HEATER AND TREAT HER LIKE A CHEERLEADER

I GREET BEEF WITH GRIEF AND DISBELIEF

MEET THE CHIEF AND THEN I SMACK EM LIKE A PETTY THIEF

I GEEK FREAKS WITH QUARTERBACK SNEAKS I TWEEK CHEEKS
FOR WEEKS

MY TECHNIQUES GET MAGNIFIQUES FROM THE CRITICS

RHYMES AINT SWEET ACIDIC, ANALYTIC GOT IT?

NAH YOU DON'T GET IT

I FIT THE BILL GOT SKILL WITH GRILL AND I WONT CHILL UNTIL

 I GOT MORE GREEN THAN CHLOROPHYLL

GO OUT IN STYLE, SHARP LIKE A NAIL FILE

AND ONCE IN A WHILE I'LL HIT YA WITH A FREESTYLE

I GOT TO ROCK LIKE COKE ON THE BLOCK

LIKE BACH, RAYMOND ST. JAQUES, JOHN HANCOCK

AND DOC, SHERLOCK, NEW KIDS ON THE BLOCK

ALFRED HITCHCOCK, I GOT STOCK IN HIP-HOP

ME AND THE FOURSOME TEARED SOME AND TOURED SOME

WEAR SOME AND WORE SOME SCARED SOME AND SCORED SOME

BUT WHEN I'M S TO THE O TO THE L O

I BELLOW MY HELLO AND THIS FELLOW AINT YELLOW

OR A SELL O...UT NO THAT AINT ME C.A.Z. IS

T.R.U.E. TO THE G.A.M.E.

G STANDS FOR GRANDEST R STANDS FOR RAW

A N AH NEVER BEEN BEAT BEFORE

D STANDS FOR DOPE MA STANDS FOR MASTER

A CAUSE I'M AWESOME AND S CAUSE I'M A SEXY BASTARD

WHAT ABOUT THE T THAT'S FOR TRUE AND E

I'M GOOD AT EVERYTHING THAT I DO

R'S FOR ROUGH AND RUGGED AND THERE'S STILL A C.A.Z.

 I WOULD SPELL THAT OUT BUT RIGHT NOW I'M KINDA LAZY

SO FROM HERE ON OUT ALL COMPETITORS BOW

AND ALL YOU CHICKENS THAT BE CLUCKIN HOW YOU LIKE ME NOW

I'M NOT GIVIN OUT NO MONEY BUT SUCKAS GET A BUCK QUICK

I'M GRANDMASTER CAZ WRONG NIGGA TO FUCK WITH!!!

You gon "See Me"

I'm the Bronx like Fordham Rd. and the Grand Concourse

I got dat real HipHop info so call me the source

But fuck 5 Mics gimme 33 and a 3rd and I'm out wit ~~~~ dirty Lee and a bird Puerto Rico.

I'm HipHop like shell toes and spray paint cans

I show love to rappers even when they aint fans

I spread the gospel of HipHop on the reg to the masses

You wanna learn how to DJ or rap attend my classes

I'm a general like Swarskoff + Colin Powel got a good heart but cross me and I'm cold n foul

and I'm a dj to@ I keep the dance floor ~~~~ poppin

~~~~ I'm McFadden & Whitehead and it aint no stoppin

112

I got a large vocabulary, good comprehension
and a gift from the Lord for keepin peoples
attention

Got a swag that says O.G. like playboys and
British

I declare violence but I'd rather fid ight
than sui ditch

My flows like spring water whats fuckin wit
dat
My shit is Evian and you fuckin wit tap

And I'm so sick the hospital is tryin to admit me
but theres nowhere to fit me I got all these girls
wit me

I'm like Willie Dynomite n Goldie the Mack
and yall aint even tryin to vache yall can't hold
me I'm back

I'm Hip Hops George Foreman cause my grill
still sellin
yall niggas quit but shit I stay ready like
a felon

I'm a microphone felon and my cd's is sell
I aint gotta do all that yellin to get inside
melon

113

Aint no need to wonder where the hell I been
As long as tables turn and there's a record
to spin
As long as winters tag and B Boys get it in
you gon see me you gon see me
As long as there's a mic yo I wont be far
if I aint puffin in the dressing room then
Im at the bar
I make sure when Im up in it yo y'all know
who we are
you gon see me , you gon see me
Dont get it fucked up you fucked up and I
know what you did
But that luck shit dont fly here its about
skills kid !

A MAN DON'T REALLY LOVE YOU IF HE HITS YOU gm caz!!!

WHAT'S UP BOO WITH YOU AND THAT CRAB ASS BROTHER
YOU GOT

DEPENDING ON HIM CAUSE YOU NEED A LOVER A LOT

A WOMAN BEATER WHO GOT YOU ON PETRO

STUCK LIKE A TRUCK AND TOO SCARED TO LET GO

SO WHAT YOU GOT A BABY BY HIM, LET THE BROTHER VISIT
IF HE FLIP

THEN LET YOUR NEW MAN FRY HIM CAUSE I BEEN DYIN TO
LET HIM HAVE IT

SO WHAT HE'S A TRCK THAT'S FOR HOOKERS AND KIDS YOU
SILLY RABBIT

AND BABY YOU DON'T NEED HIS LOOT

YOU GOT A JOB YOU GET YOUR OWN SO GIVE THAT

NIGGA THE BOOT AND MOVE AHEAD WITH YOUR LIFE

HOW YOU EVER GONNA HAVE A MAN OR BE SOMEBODY'S
WIFE

THE NIGGA SWEATS YOU LIKE A CARDIGAN

AND IF HE DON'T BREAK YOUR NECK HE'S BOUND TO BREAK
YOUR HEART AGAIN

YOUR KID IS TWO HE'LL NEVER MISS EM   A
BETTER MAN WILL COME ALONG AND STAY IF YOU DON'T
DISS HIM

BUT AINT NOBODY PLAYIN SECOND FIDDLE

TO AN OLD RELATIONSHIP BECAUSE YOU'RE THROWIN
YOUR KID IN THE MIDDLE

I THOUGHT YOU HAD A BETTER GRIP

AND IF YOU CAN'T KEEP YOUR BOAT AFLOAT THEN

ABANDON SHIP

AND SUGAR TAKE YOUR BABY WIT YA AND REMEMBER A
MAN DON'T REALLY LOVE YOU IF HE HIT YA

YOUR LITTLE BOY IS GETTIN BIGGER AND HE'S STARTIN TO
NOTICE A LOT

HE AINT WORRIED IF HE'S GONNA GET SODAS OR NOT

HE KNOWS THE NOISE MEANS POPS KICKIN ASSES

AND HE KEEPS MOMMY HIDIN BEHIND DARK GLASSES

HE GOES TO BED EVERY NIGHT AND HE CRY

AND HE PRAY THAT THIS AINT THE DAY THAT HIS MOMMY
DIE

OR GET HURT REAL BAD BEACAUSE OF SOMETHING THAT
HAPPENED THAT MADE HIS DADDY MAD

CAUSE HE DON'T UNDERSTAND THE VIOLENCE

INFLICTED ON HIS MOM BY HIS DAD SO HE SITS IN SILENCE

SCARED AND CONFUSED THINKING MAYBE IT WAS
SOMETHING THAT HE DID THAT GOT HIS MOMMY ABUSED

SO MOM BEFORE HE GETS A GUN

PACK YOUR STUFF AND YOUR KID AND DON'T WALK

AWAY FROM HIM.. RUN HURRY AND GET HIM OUT THE
PICTURE

AND REMEMBER AMAN DON'T REALLY LOVE YOU IF HE HIT
YA

IT'S NOT YOUR FAULT NOBODY'S GOT THE RIGHT TO BEAT
ON A FEMALE

A MAN SHOULD TALK IT OUT IF HE CALLS HIMSELF A REAL
MALE

AND IF HE CAN'T RELY ON WITS YOU NEED TO SLIDE CAUSE
I KNOW YOU GET TIRED OF HIM CATCHIN FITS

YOU NEED TO FIND ANOTHER MATE CAUSE LIKE THE SONG
GO

IT'S A THIN LINE BETWEEN LOVE AND HATE

FIRST YOU IN LOVE AND HAVIN FUN WIT HIM AND THEN HE
FLIP AND YOU GOTTA CALL 911 TO GET HIM

THAT AINT NO LIFE FOR YOU BOO

MAKE UP AINT SUPPOSED TO BE TO COVER UP YOUR BLACK
AND BLUE

YOU SHOULD'NT HAVE TO LIVE IN FEAR

GIVE HIM HIS WALKING PAPERS TELL HIM HIS ASS IS
OUTTA HERE

AND IF YOU'RE SCARED LET SOMEBODY KNOW CAUSE AINT
NO LOVIN IN THE WORLD SHOULD MAKE YOU STAY WHEN
YOU GOTTA GO

FIND A RELATIONSHIP THAT FITS YA AND REMEMBER

A MAN DON'T REALLY LOVE YOU IF HE HITS YA!!!

Before?

Caz

Before rap was a game or HipHop was a nation

Before Lauren Hill began her miseducation

Before Milk was chillin or PE brought the noise

Before Heavy D and the Boys

Before the roof caught on fire

Before fresh was the word

Before Whodini and friends or Roxanne's revenge

Before the freaks came out at night

Before say ho

Before the Crash Crew was rockin on the radio

Before Whitney, Mariah, J-Lo and Janet

Before Bam and the Soulsonic Force rocked the planet

Before these are the breaks
Before hard times
Before the Sugarhill Gang and before Super
Rhymes
Before Reaganomics before rappers got
shot in their stomachs
Before you found Hip Hop in comics
Before g's Before weed was trees
Before goin raw dog gave you a deadly
disease)
Before haters Before thugs and perpetrators
Before the alphas and before the betas
Before beepers and cell phones and retro
gear
fed ex, food stamps and metro cards
Before cops was 5-0 or gats was answers
Before the B-Boys turned into
"BREAKDANCERS"

Before Leos was crazy before out
turned to Swayzee
Before I said it's hot, humid and hazy
Before all the bullshit and lay no means
get it twisted
My name is HipHop and I have always
existed
In this physical form or in the essence
of rhyme...

Grandmaster Caz niggas greatest of
All Time

The Art of Rap

I been down wit this since the
start of rap
I guess you can say I played a big
part of ~~that~~ rap
I've not only been the brain but the
heart of rap
And it beats just like a drum and that's the
art of rap
I been known to flip flows like bricks and
pancakes
And yeah I seen my share of tricks and
handshakes
by chicks and bandmates with a different
agenda
female and male snakes and some great
pretenders

but trust me on this for as long as
I'm breathin
I'm gon check a wack rapper
or call out a heathen
I'm gon lead by example with this
hot shit I'm spittin
And you just saw me write it
So you ~~know~~ damn right it's written

That's part of the art of rap
in twenty minutes flat.
Write a rhyme in real time
now what's fuckin wit dat
So y'all can fall back from
that old cat dont get it twisted
the N/C train just left the station
I was on it, you missed it.

"NAME GAME"

Mizza	Tony	Chase	A.D.
Is A	Boney	Bass	Beatty
Scissor	Joanie	Face	Lady
Rza	Money	Case	Shooty
Gza	Pony	Lace	Haiti
Lizard	Roni	Mase	Eighty
Wizard	Song	Pace	
		Race	

Money	L	K.G.	NIGGAS
Bunny	Bell	Agee	FIGURES
Funny	Cell	Eazy E	CIGAS
Honey	Fell	Hood E	TRIGGERS
Runny	Gel	Sage	ZIGGAS
Sunny	Hell		
	Mel		

Broken	Sell	Bitches
Jokin	Tell	Ditches
Pokin	Well	Glitches
Soakin	Yell	Hitch is
Token		Nitches
Smokin		Pitches
Yokin		Riches
		Stitches
		Witches

Hip Hop didn't invent anything.
Hip Hop re-invented everything.

Grandmaster Caz

NEW TITLES FROM WAHIDA CLARK PRESENTS

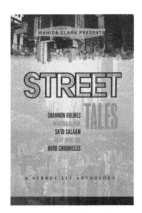

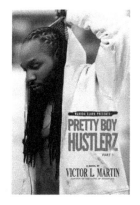

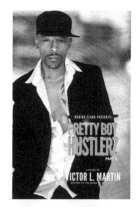

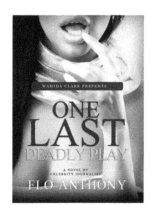

#READIT

WWW.WCLARKPUBLISHING.COM

CPSIA information can be obtained
at www.ICGtesting.com
Printed in the USA
BVHW020040211019
561601BV00001B/1/P

9 781947 732360